Return to Room 237

BONHOMME

for Anne

BONHOMME

Story and Pictures by

Laurent de Brunhoff

Translated from the French by

Richard Howard

Pantheon Books

5 868

Emilie's house is at the foot of the red mountain. There are no bushes on the mountain, and there is no stream. But there is a tree. And Emilie watches that tree. She watches it through a telescope, from the roof of her house.

Beside the tree, Emilie sees a
little man. He is a funny little man.
It looks as though he has a thorn
growing out of the back of his head.

Sometimes Emilie sees him walking,
but most of the time he stays beside
the tree, as if he were thinking.

One night, sitting on the edge of her bed,
Emilie thinks: "I'd like to know why
that little man stays up there all alone.
I'll have to climb the mountain."

And so she sets out. She climbs up and up,
as fast as she can, without stopping,
without looking back.

Finally she reaches the
very top of the mountain.
Beside the tree, the
little man is standing,
as round as he can be,
with a sharp spike
growing out of the back
of his head. He looks
gentle and shy, and he stares
at Emilie intently.

"Bonhomme," Emilie says,
for that is the name of a
little man in French, and
Emilie is a French girl.
"Bonhomme, come here . . ."

Is it because he is very happy?
Is it because he is something of a clown?
The little man begins to run
around the tree. He runs so fast
that Emilie thinks she is seeing
eight little men running
around the tree!

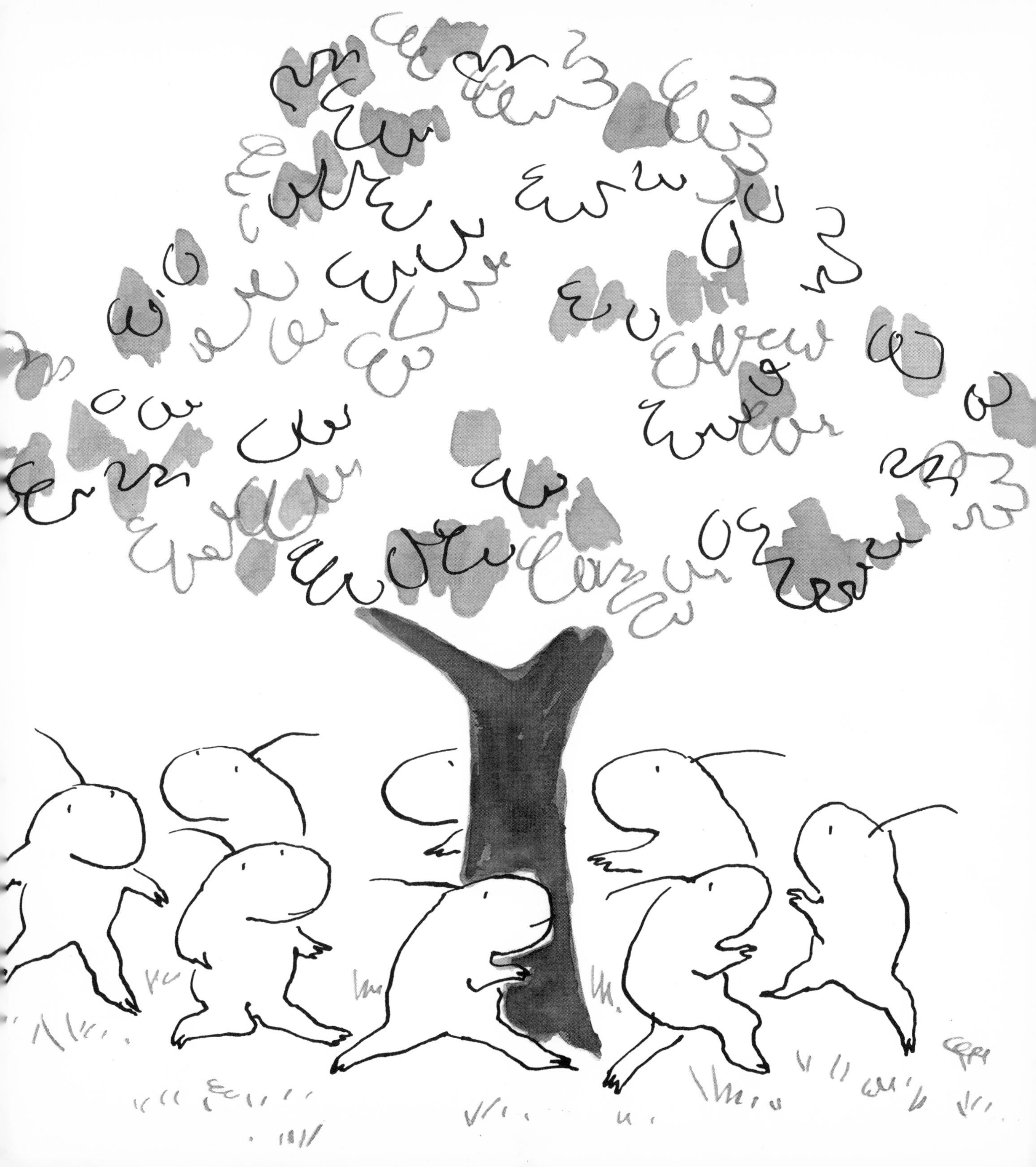

He makes a bouquet of the dry grasses that
grow on the mountain and gives it to
Emilie. "Oh, that's nice of you, Bonhomme.
Is it all right if I call you Bonhomme?"

The two of them take a walk around the mountaintop.

Bonhomme shows his friend the lovely view.

Emilie opens her bag and shares
with Bonhomme a little loaf of
bread, a chocolate bar and some
pieces of sugar.

They stay a long time....

When Emilie doesn't come home, her parents
go out and look for her everywhere.

But they don't find her, because they
never think of going all the way
to the top of the mountain.

Then they notify the Mayor

and the Mayor summons a meeting of the town council.

The town councilors send the police
up to the mountain. The police find Emilie. . . .

And they catch Bonhomme in a net.

Bonhomme is shut up in the zoo.
He is very unhappy, and he cries.
His spike is beginning to wilt, and
Emilie is worried. "Don't get sick,
Bonhomme. Be brave! I'm going
to see the Mayor. You won't have
to stay in the zoo, I promise you."

"Mr. Mayor," Emilie says, "Bonhomme won't hurt anyone, he's my friend." The Mayor listens to Emilie, and he doesn't know what to say. After thinking it over a long time, as he walks up and down in his office, he says to her: "Emilie, I will agree to let Bonhomme loose. But on one condition—he'll have to put a cork on the end of his spike."

Emilie runs to the zoo. The keeper, who
has already been notified, opens the cage.
Bonhomme lets a cork be put on the end
of his spike, and gets on the bus to go
to his friend's house.

Bonhomme feels better there.
Emilie's parents speak gently
in order not to frighten him.

Bonhomme goes "hummmm" when
Emilie gives him some hot chocolate.
He likes good things to eat.

Bonhomme is fascinated

by the bathroom mirror.

Emilie's Papa offers him cigars.
That is what Bonhomme likes best.
He smokes two at a time.

That night, when everyone is going to bed,
Emilie decides that Bonhomme should
sleep on the living-room couch. The cork
bothers him a little—he is not used to it.
So Emilie gives him a big, soft pillow.

Bonhomme sleeps very well that night.
But the next morning, when Emilie
is away at school, he gets bored.
Emilie's Mama sees him leave the
house without making a sound, and
she doesn't dare try to stop him. . . .

Bonhomme does not come back.
He left his cork behind the door.

But ever since that day,
Emilie often goes walking on the mountain.
And when she comes back she says,
with a funny little face,
"I saw Bonhomme today."